D1358737

HANDS-ON LETTERS
Match-ups

by Marilynn G. Barr

Publisher: Roberta Suid
Production: Little Acorn & Associates, Inc.

MATCH-UPS
Entire contents copyright © 2004
by Monday Morning Books, Inc.

For a complete catalog, write to the address below:
Monday Morning Books, Inc.
PO Box 1134
Inverness, CA 94937

Call our toll-free number: 1-800-255-6049
E-mail us at: MMBooks@aol.com
Visit our Web site:
http://www.mondaymorningbooks.com

ISBN 1-57612-193-3

Printed in the United States of America
9 8 7 6 5 4 3

Contents

Introduction

Match-ups includes alphabet match boards, matching alphabet cards for each letter of the alphabet, and a variety of project ideas for creative skills practice fun. Blank cards are provided to program with cut-out letters, children's names, or alternate pictures that do and do not match the accompanying match board. Match-ups are designed for children to color and cut out for lots of alphabet skills practice fun. For cutting ease, odd-shaped patterns are positioned within easy-to-cut-out geometric forms. Children will learn to recognize and match alphabet pictures and letters and develop their fine motor skills. Additional Match-ups project ideas can be found on pages 62-63.

Provide children with crayons, markers, scissors, and glue to make Match-ups Folders, Vests, Portfolios, and more. Create an alphabet practice workstation with Poster-sized Match-ups, Cereal Box Match-ups, and a deck of cards to play Match-ups Concentration. Use the Workstation Supplies List on page 6 to take inventory of supplies on-hand and needed supplies. Reproduce the Request For Supplies form on page 64 for children to take home asking parents to help stock your workstation.

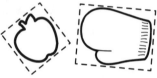  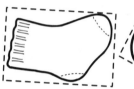

Match-ups

Provide children with materials to make individual alphabet skills practice folders.

Materials:

Match-ups boards and cards	manila file folders
crayons or markers	scissors
glue	letter-sized envelopes
construction paper	

Program the blank cards of the matching card set with cut-out letters, children's names, or alternate alphabet pictures. Then reproduce, laminate, and cut out a set of cards for each child. Reproduce a construction paper match board for each child to color, cut out, and glue to the inside of a manila file folder. Help each child write the matching letter on the front of his or her folder. Encourage children to decorate the front of folders with crayons, markers, and a variety of craft supplies. Then help them glue a letter-sized envelope to the back of each of their folders to store matching card sets. Do not glue the flap to the folder.

Children draw and place only the cards that match on each space of the match board.

Poster-sized Match-ups

Make poster-sized match boards and cards to display in an alphabet skills practice center.

Materials:

Match-ups boards and cards   poster board
scissors   crayons or markers
glue

Enlarge and transfer match boards and cards (pp. 7-58) onto poster board. Color the match boards, then glue the matching cards to the spaces on each match board.

My Alphabet Match-ups Portfolio

Materials:

oak tag   crayons or markers   hole punch
yarn   stapler   Match-ups boards and cards
scissors   resealable plastic bag

Provide each child with a large sheet of oak tag. Have children fold oak tag to form a portfolio (diagram A). Encourage children to use crayons or markers to decorate the outside of their portfolios. Help each child punch two holes along the top of his or her portfolio (diagram B). Measure, cut, and tie a length of yarn through each set of holes to form portfolio handles.

Reproduce oak tag match boards for each child to color and cut out. Program the blank cards of the matching card set with cut-out letters, children's names, or alternate alphabet pictures. Then reproduce, laminate, and cut out a set for each child. Provide large resealable plastic bags for children to store each set of Match-ups inside their portfolios.

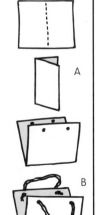

Alphabet Match Game

Reproduce the match board and cards on pages 59-61 for children to play an Alphabet Match game.

Materials:

Match Board boards and cards	file folder	scissors
crayons or markers	glue	colored construction paper
cellophane tape		

Reproduce, color, and cut out match boards. Glue the match boards to the inside of a file folder. Reproduce, laminate, and cut out colored construction paper cards (p. 61). Measure, cut, and tape a construction paper pocket to the back of the folder for card storage.

Two to four children can play a game of Alphabet Match. Have children place the cards face down. Each child, in turn, draws a card to place on the matching letter space. Encourage children to say the word that matches the alphabet picture to determine the beginning letter sound before placing the card on the matching letter space. Play continues until all the cards are placed on matching letter spaces. Help children check their matches.

Match-ups Workstation Supplies List

Match-ups boards and cards	brown grocery bags	cotton swabs
yarn	crayons	craft sticks
ribbon	markers	Velcro (adhesive)
twine	glitter	pipe cleaners
shoelaces	glitter pens	paint
hole punches	wiggle eyes	paintbrushes
scissors	letter-sized envelopes	wallpaper scraps
buttons	sticky dots	glue
pom poms	construction paper	_____
resealable plastic bags	cotton balls	_____
cereal boxes (empty)	sequins	_____
star stickers	index cards	_____

Apple Tree Match Board

Apple Cards

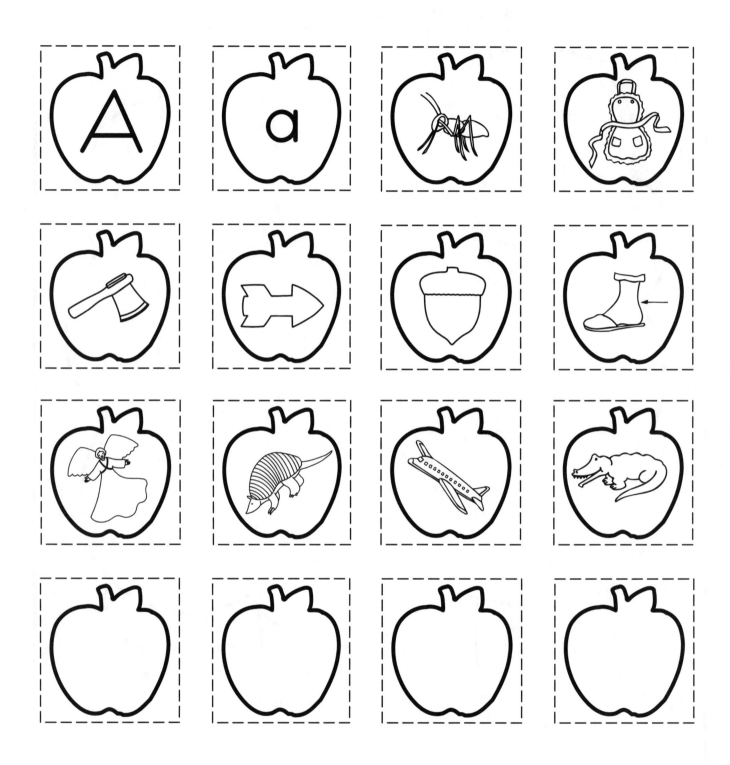

Boat Match Board

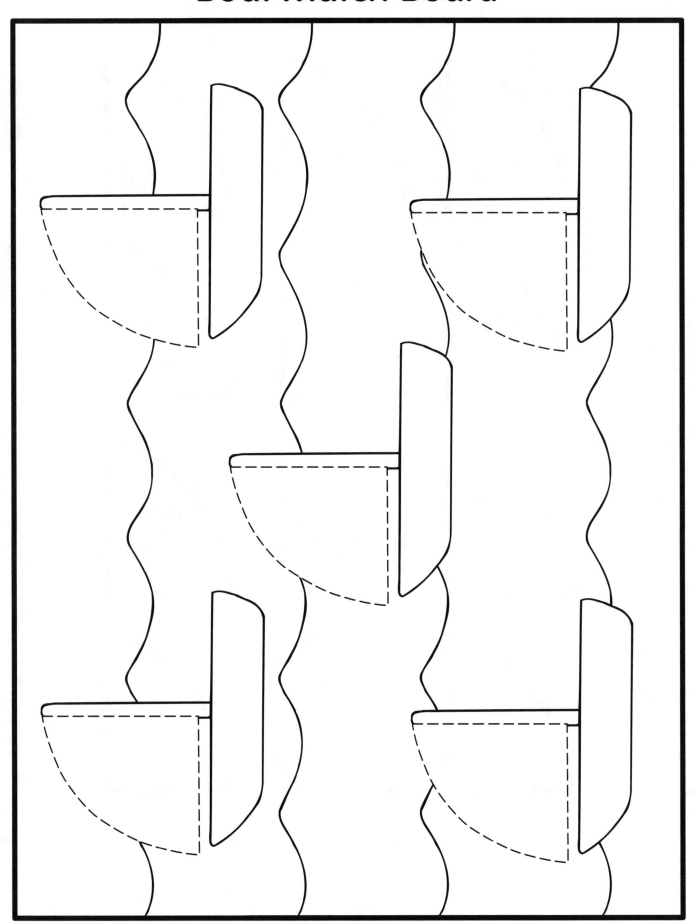

Boat Cards

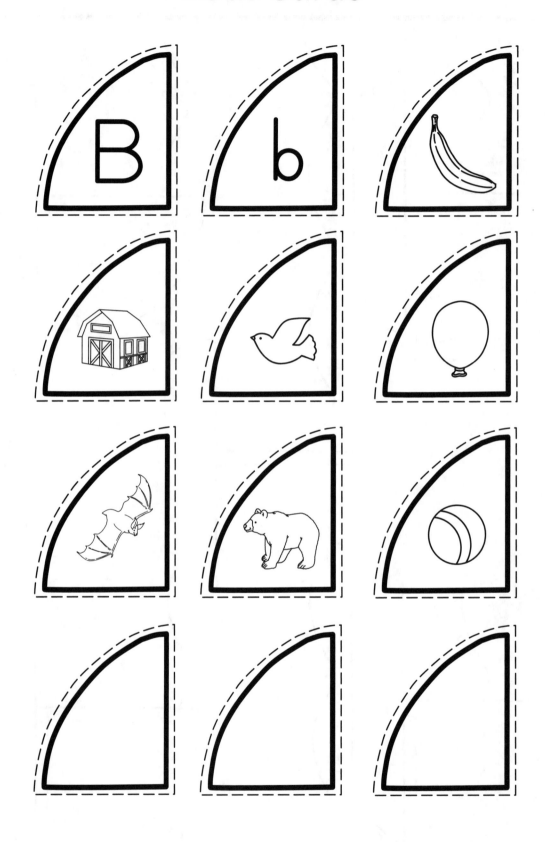

Cookie Jar Match Board

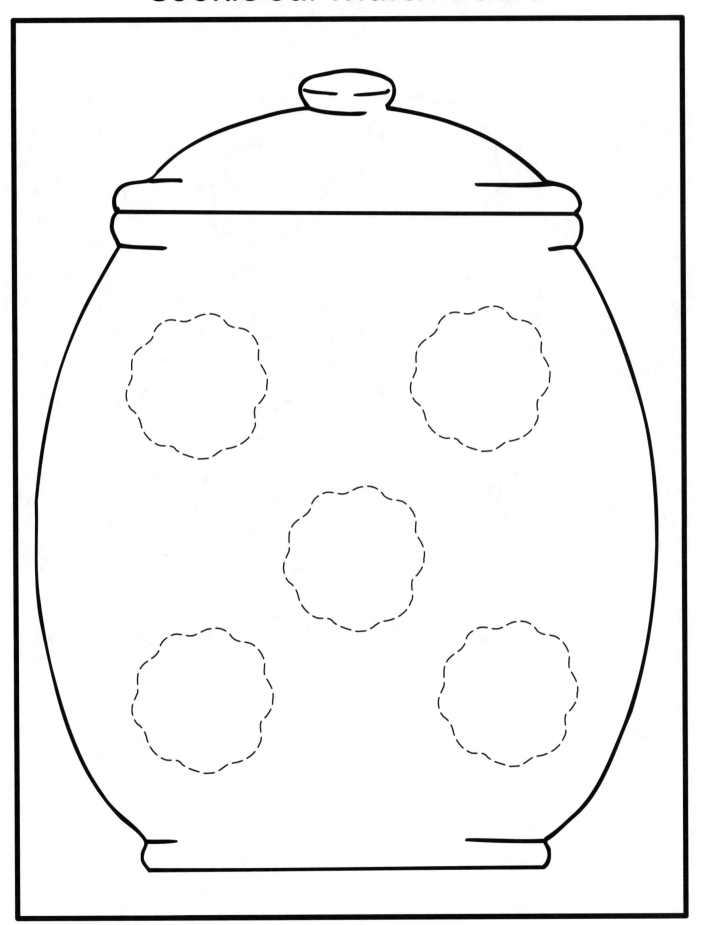

Cookie Cards

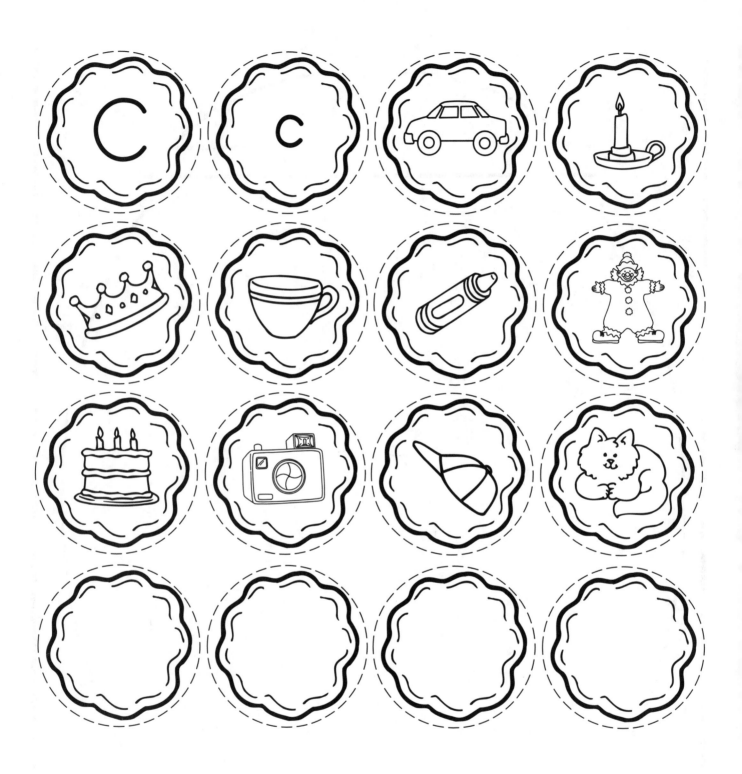

Match-ups • ©2004 Monday Morning Books, Inc.

Dragon Spot Match Board

Dragon Spot Cards

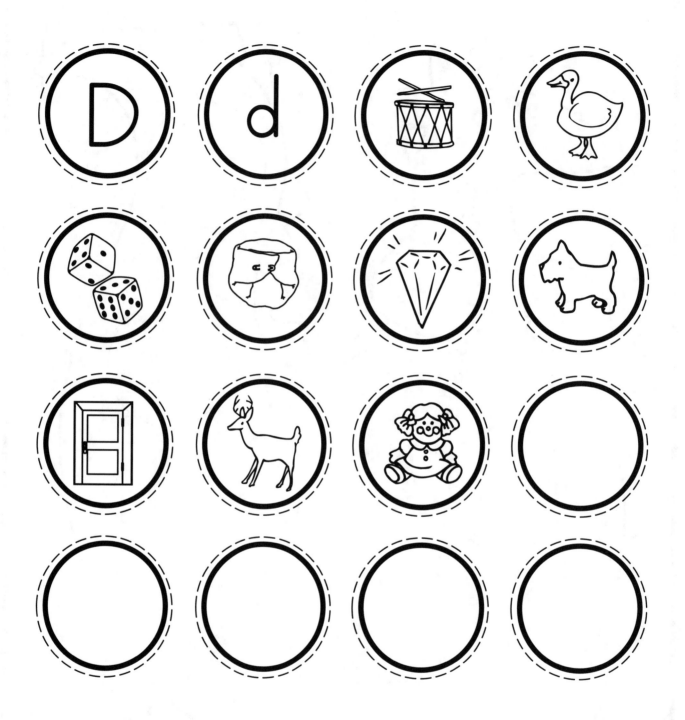

Egg Basket Match Board

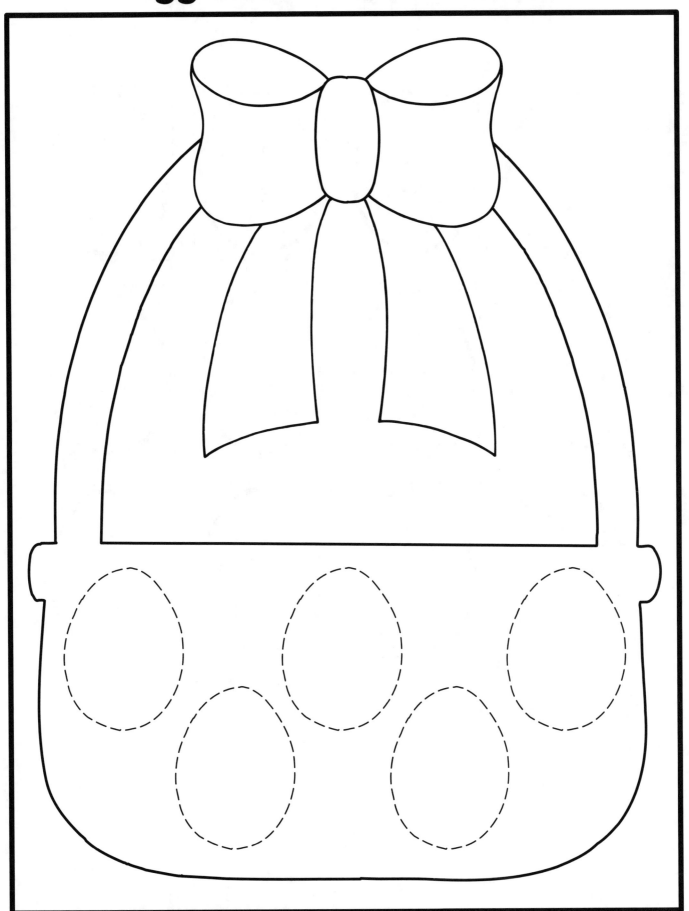

Egg Cards

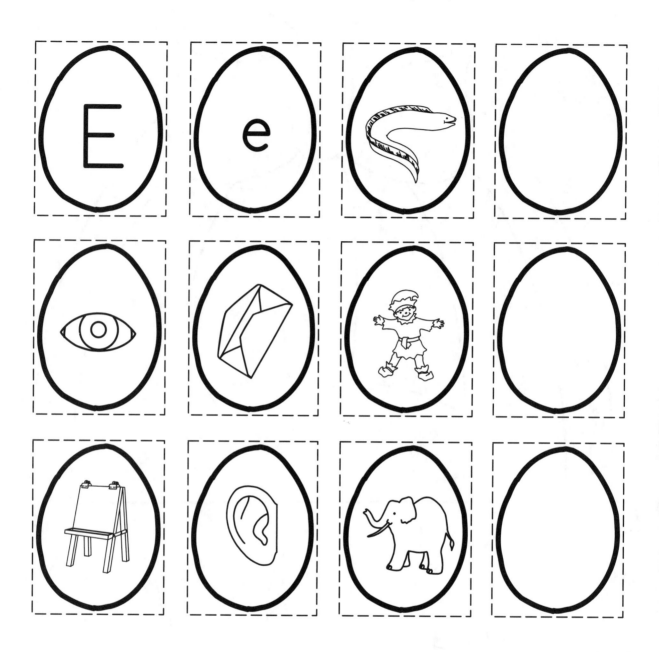

Flower Match Board

Flower Match Cards

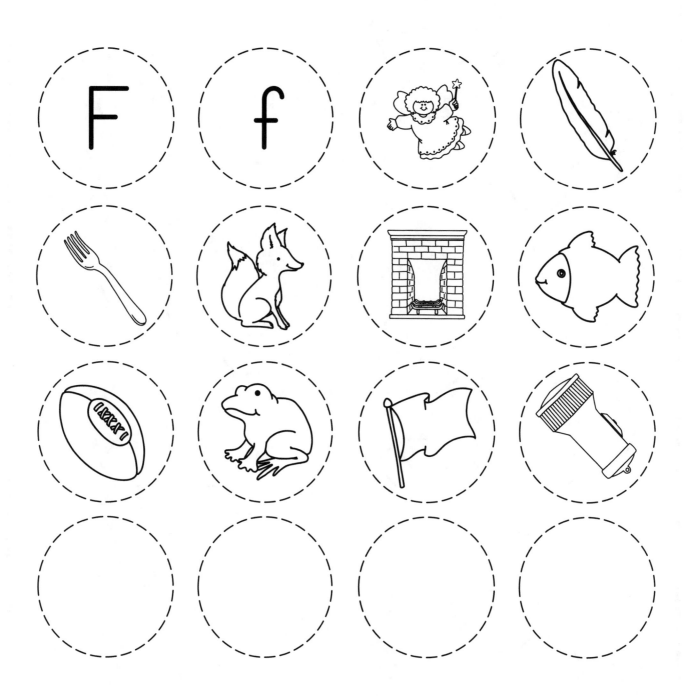

Gumball Machine Match Board

Gumball Cards

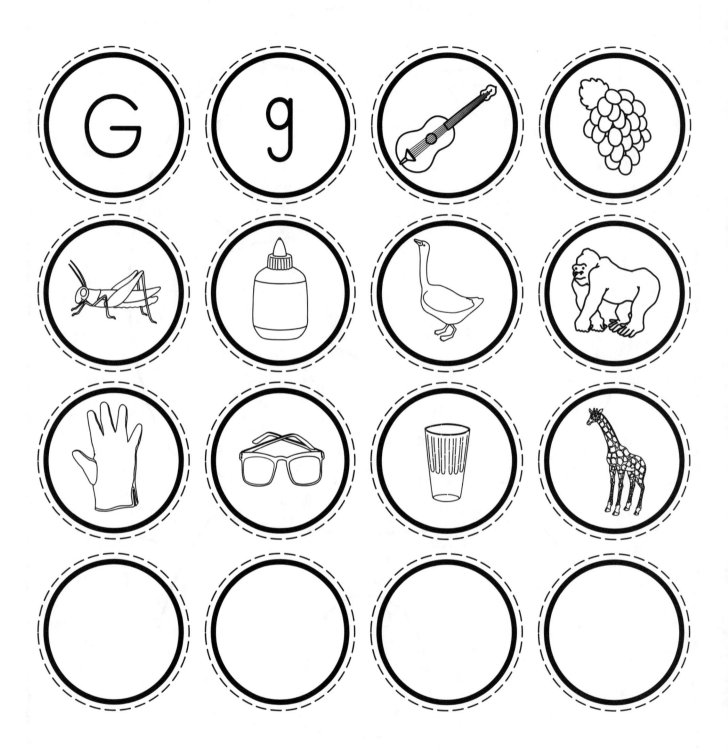

Hippos Wearing Hats Match Board

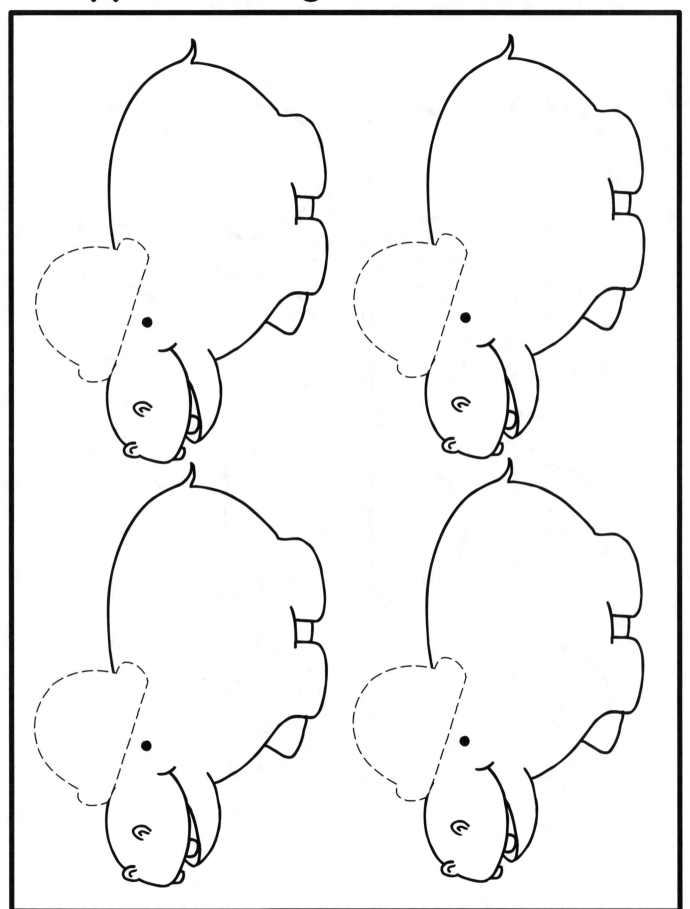

Hat Cards

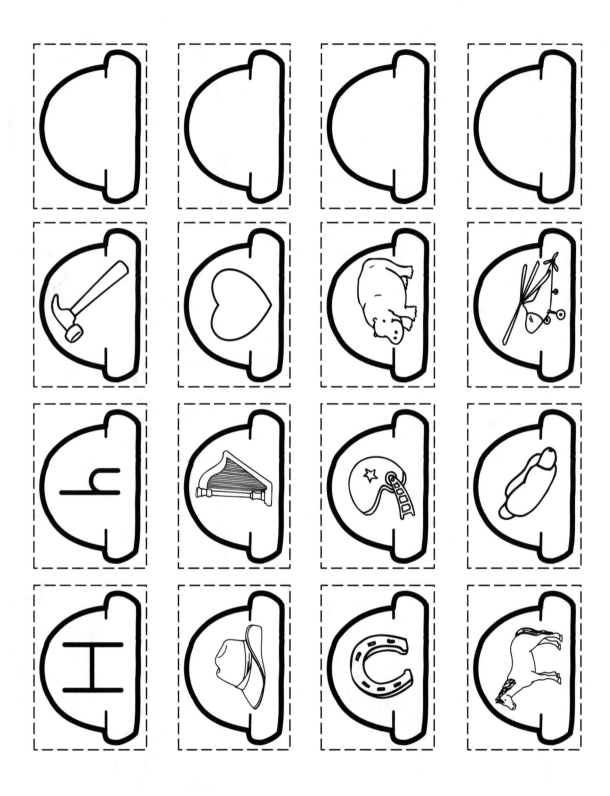

Igloo Match Board

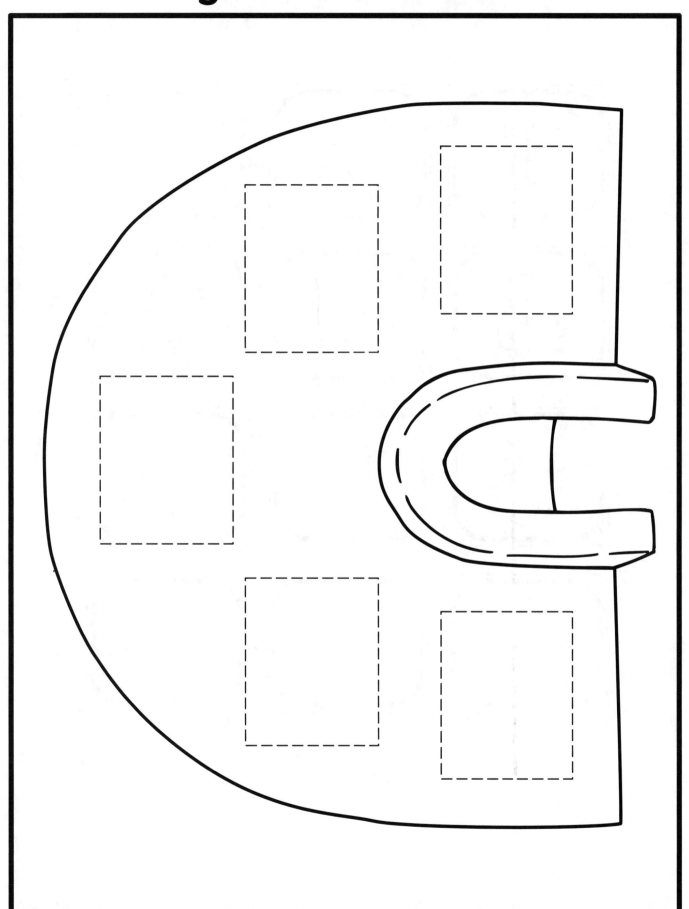

Ice Cube Cards

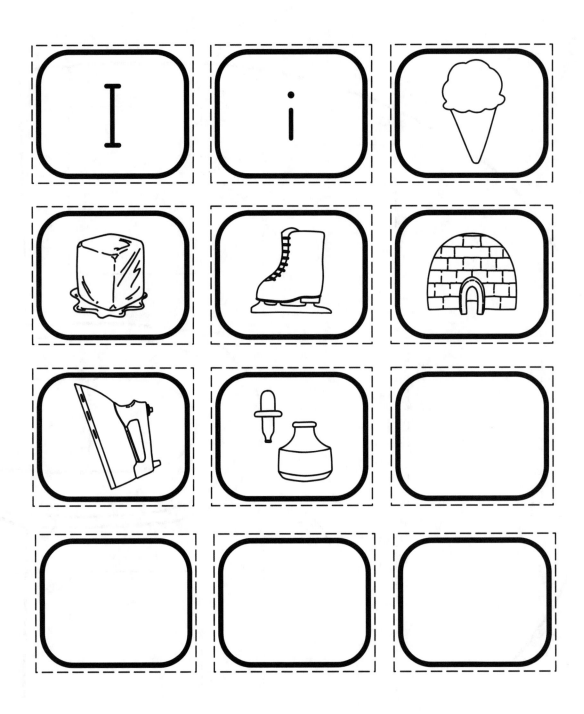

Jellybean Jar Match Board

Jellybean Cards

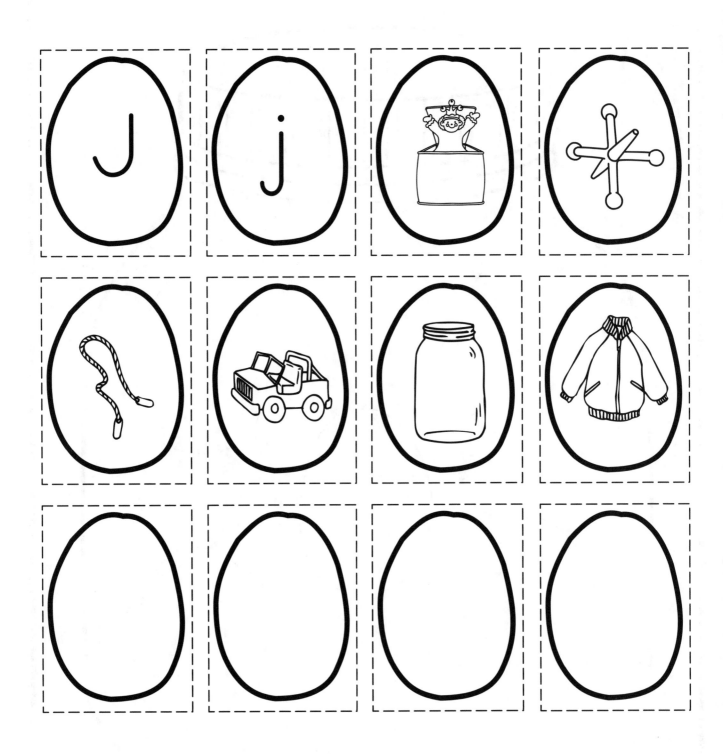

Kite Flying Match Board

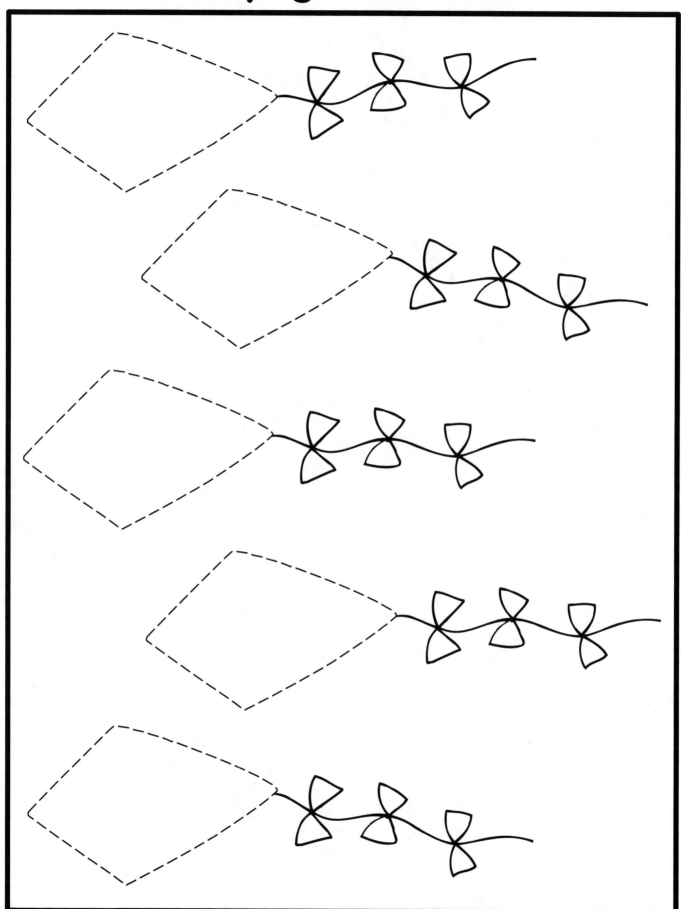

Kite Cards

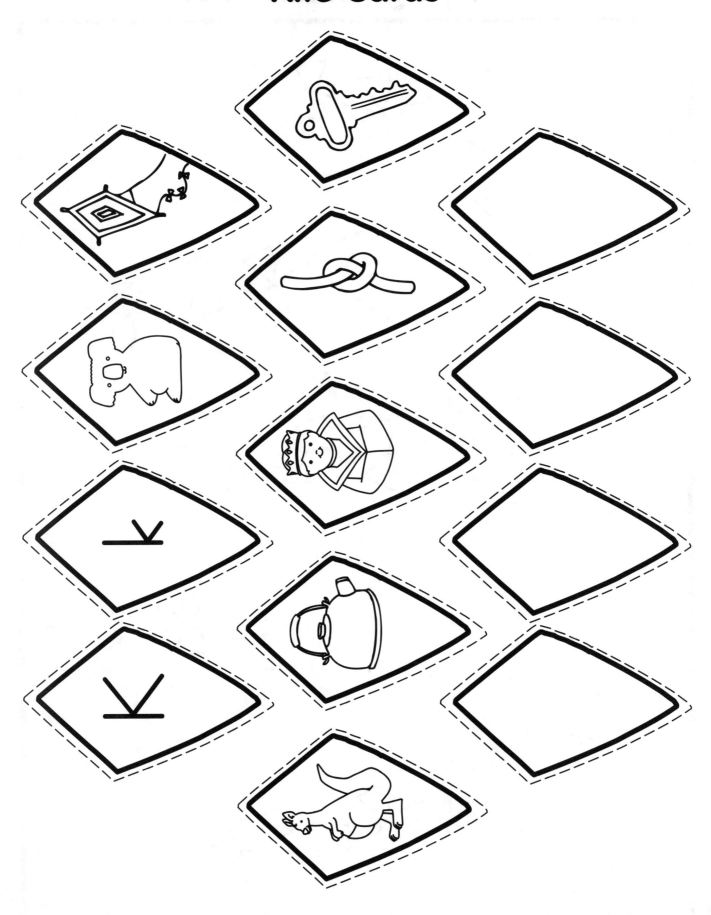

Ladybug Match Board

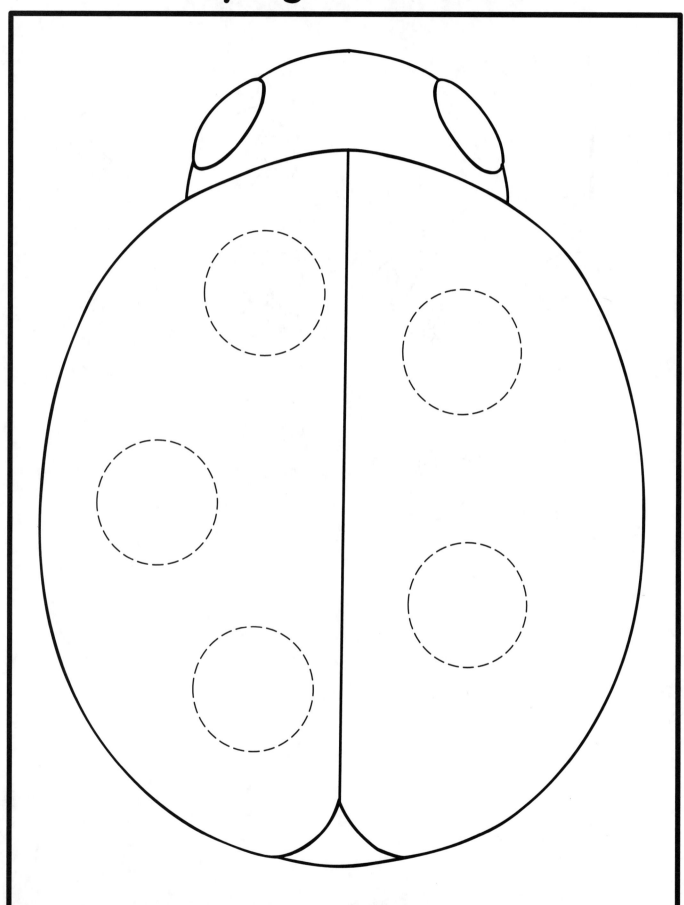

Spot Cards

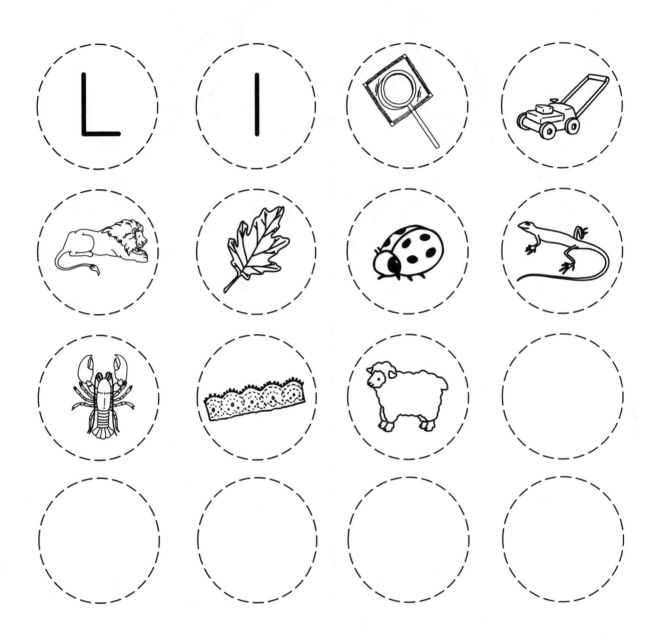

Mitten Match Board

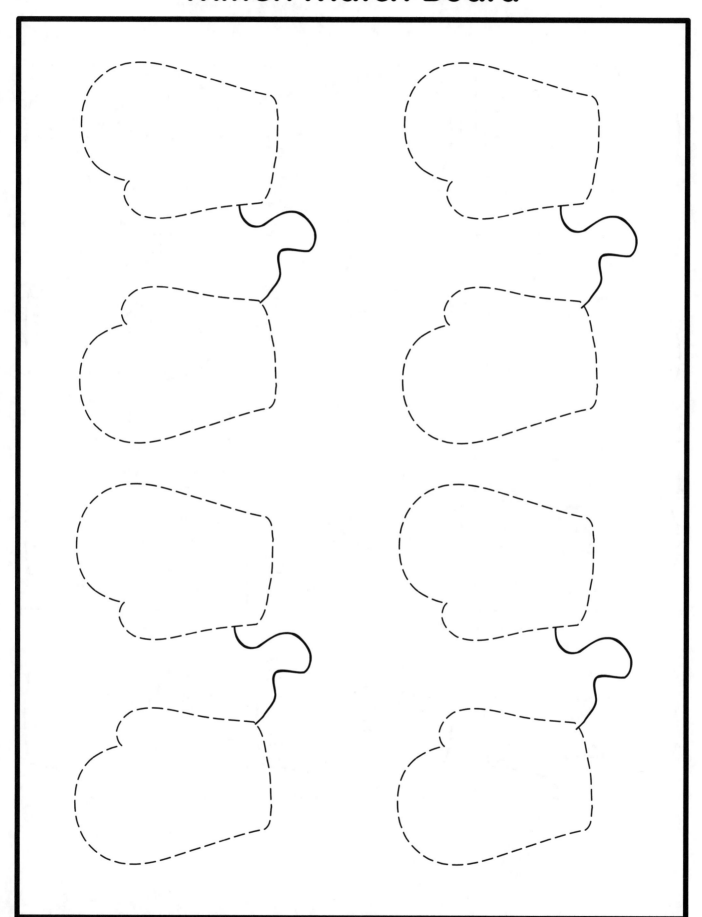

Mitten Cards

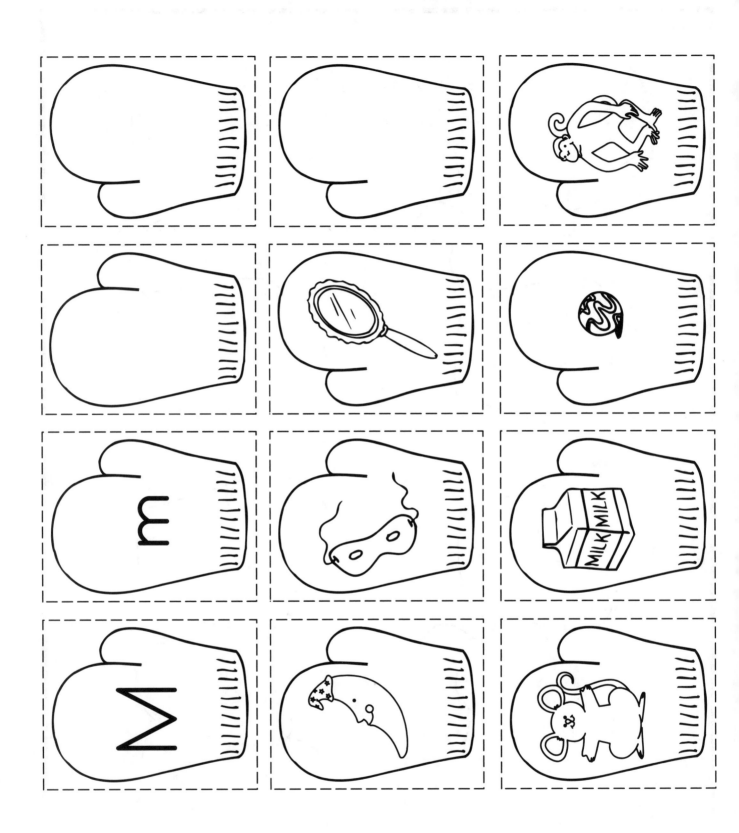

Birds in Nests Match Board

Nest Cards

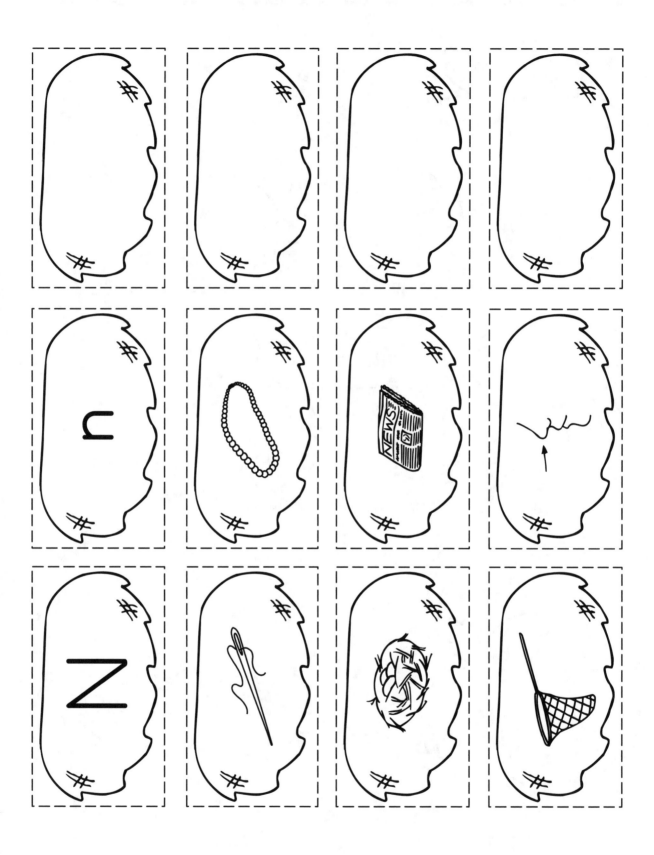

Owls Wearing Overalls Match Board

Overalls Cards

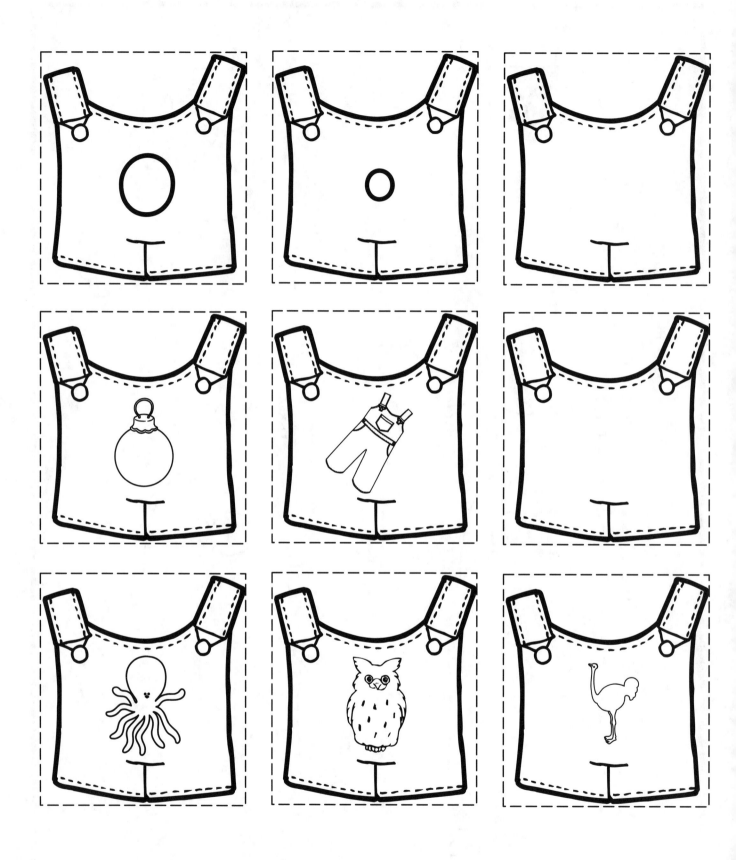

Peanuts in a Shell Match Board

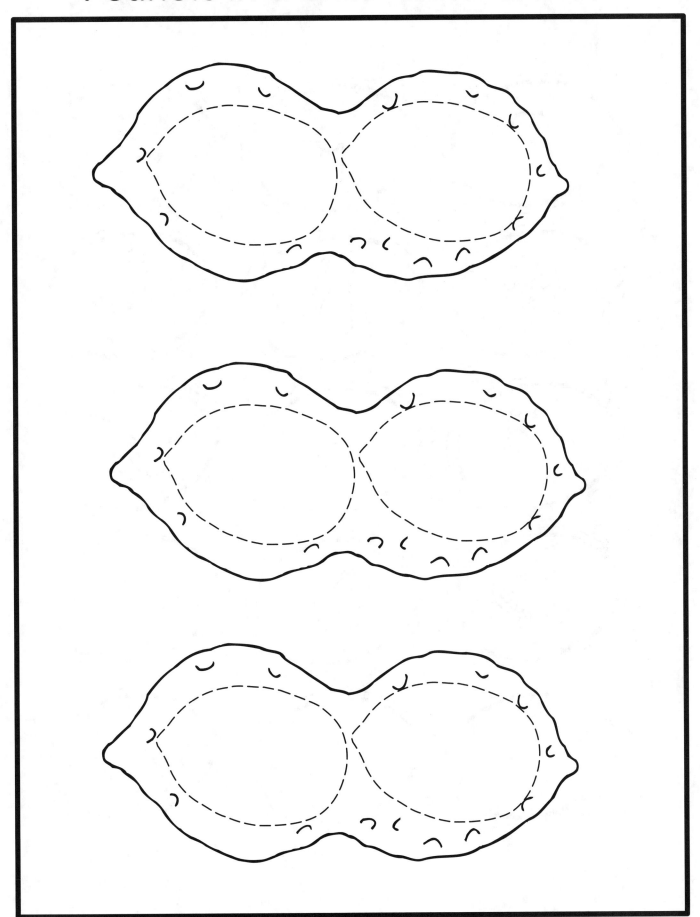

Peanut Cards

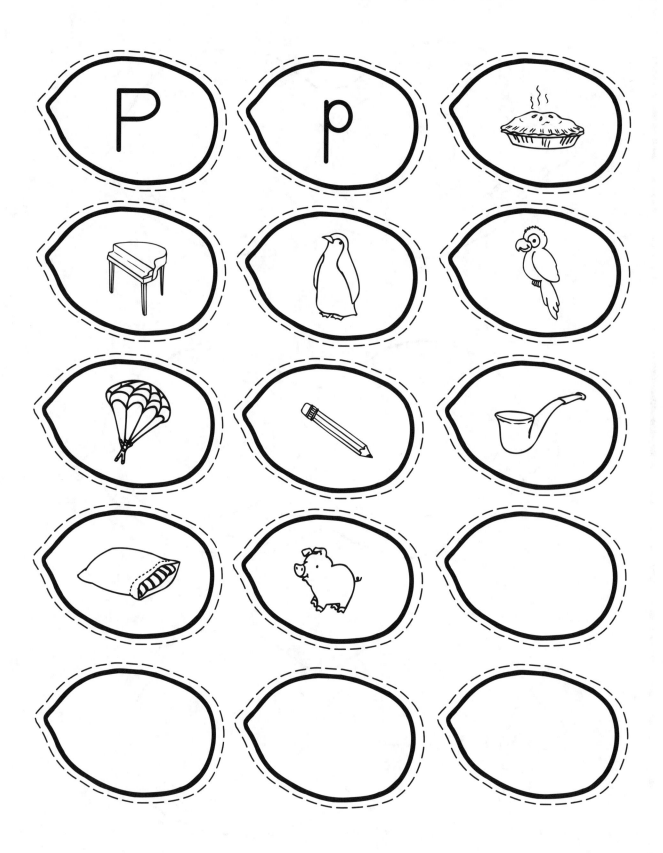

Quilt Match Board

Quilt Square Cards

Rabbit Ears Match Board

Rabbit Ear Cards

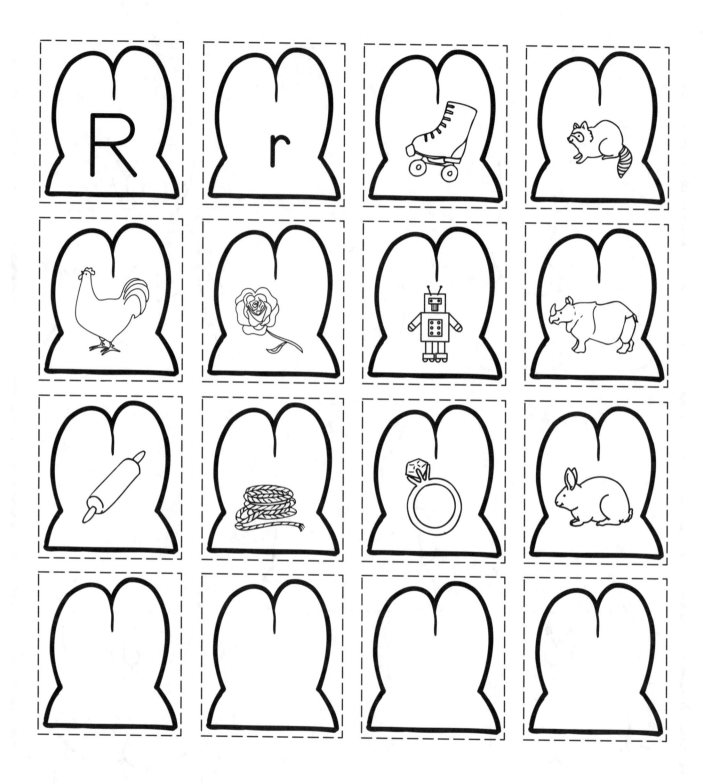

Socks Match Board

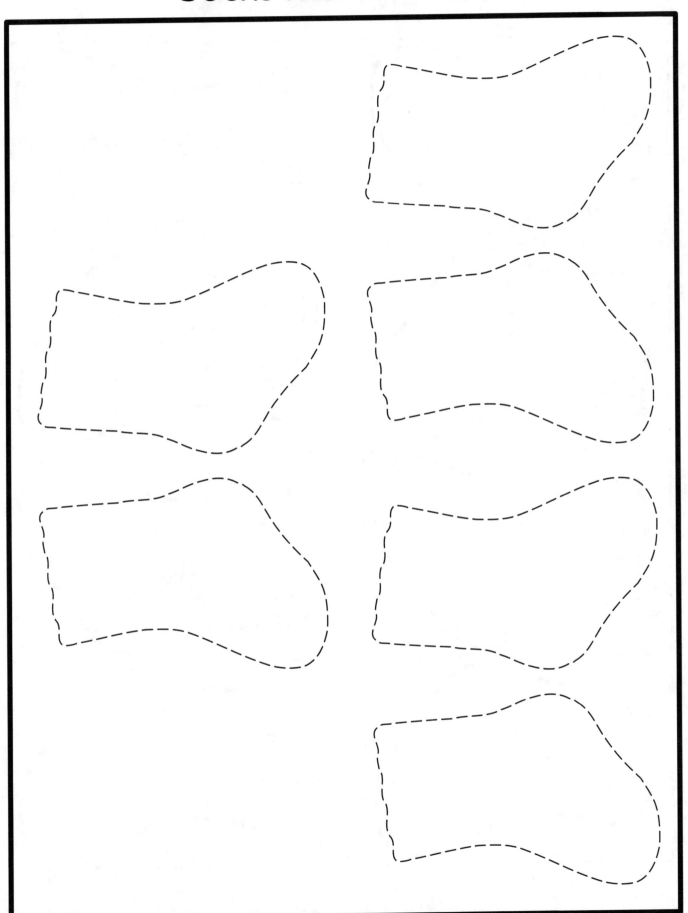

Sock Cards

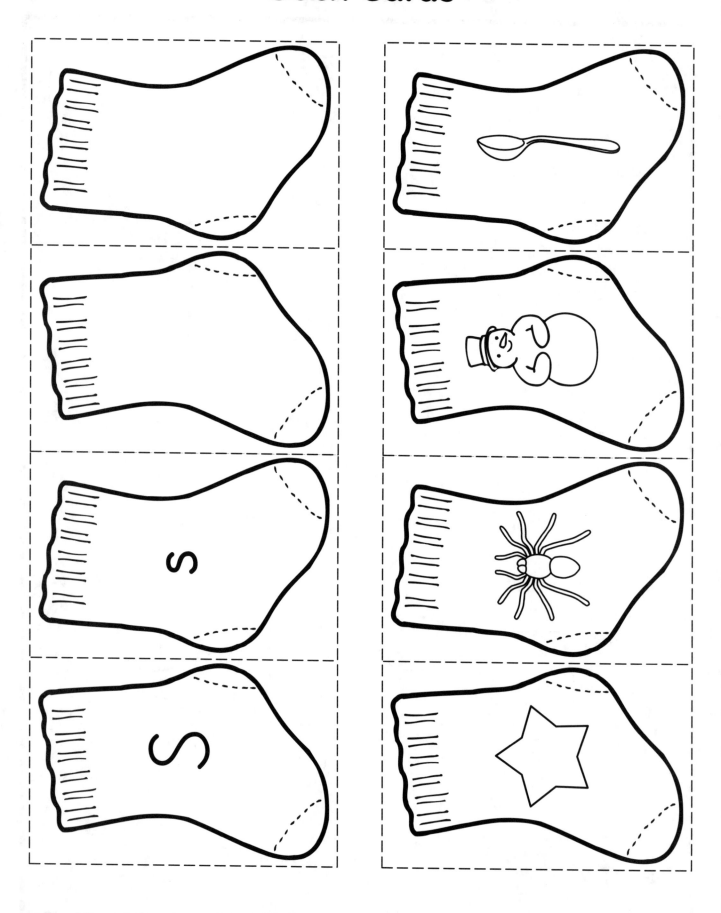

Tea Cup Match Board

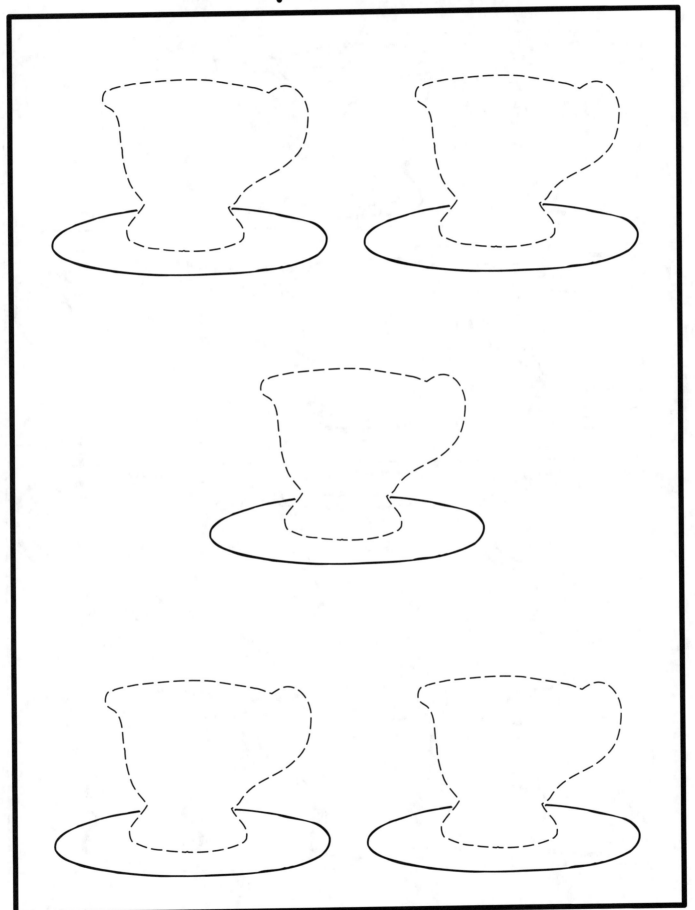

Tea Cup Cards

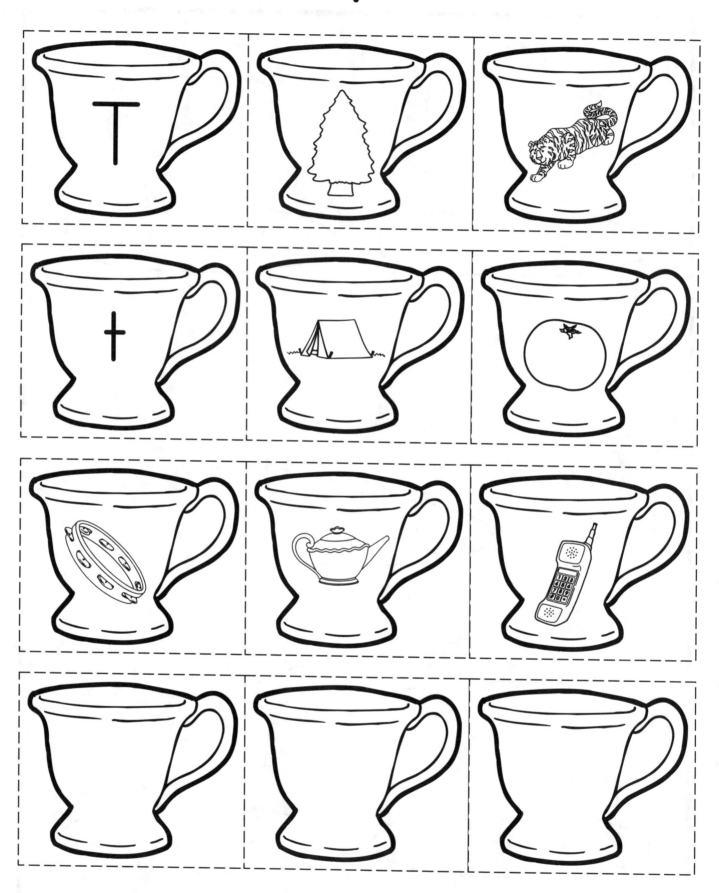

Umbrella Match Board

Raindrop Cards

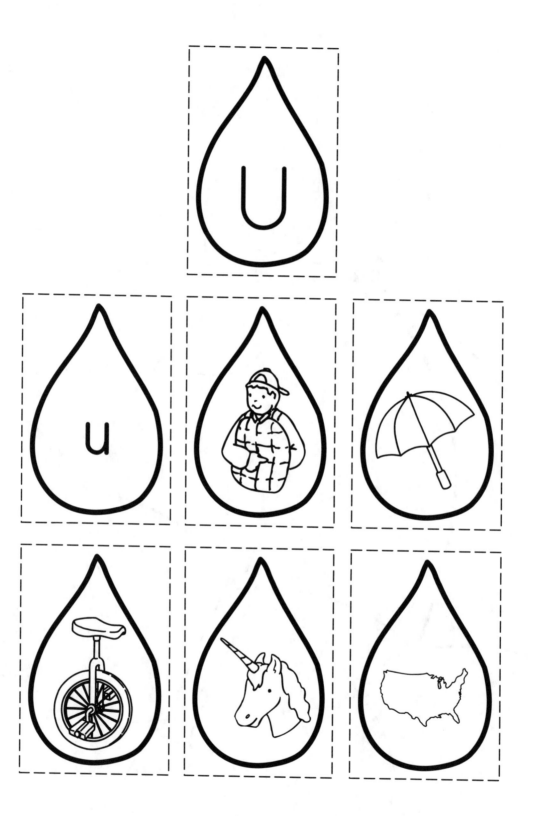

Buttons on a Vest Match Board

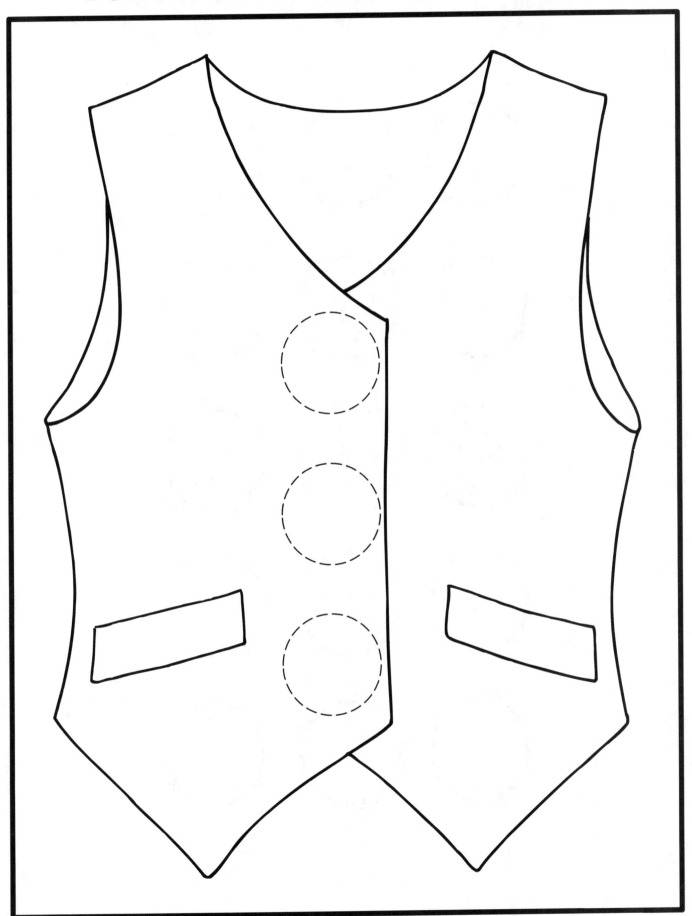

Button Cards

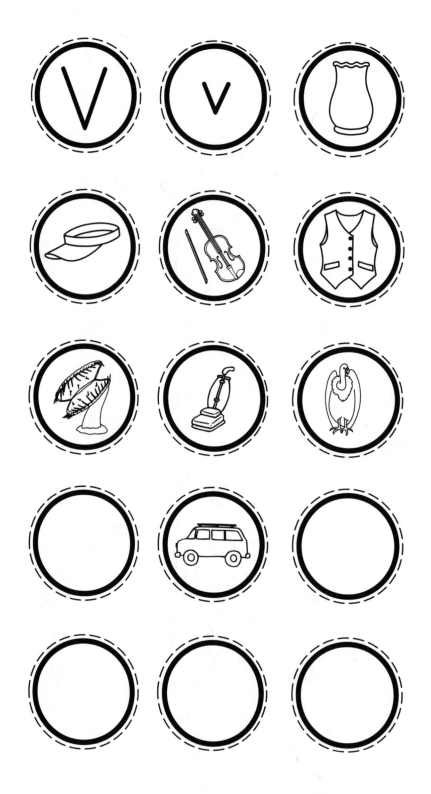

Wagon Wheels Match Board

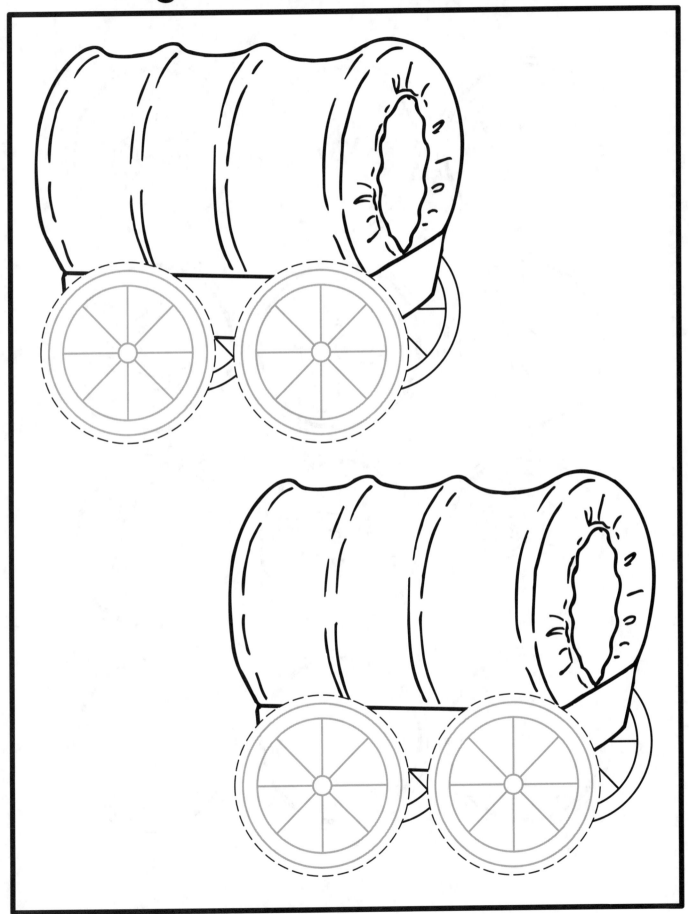

Wheel Cards

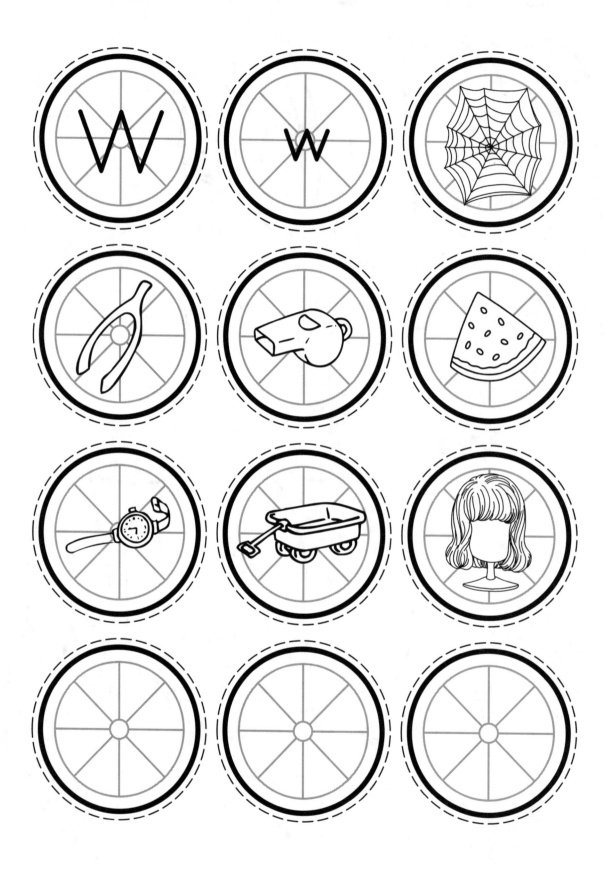

X Marks the Spot Match Board

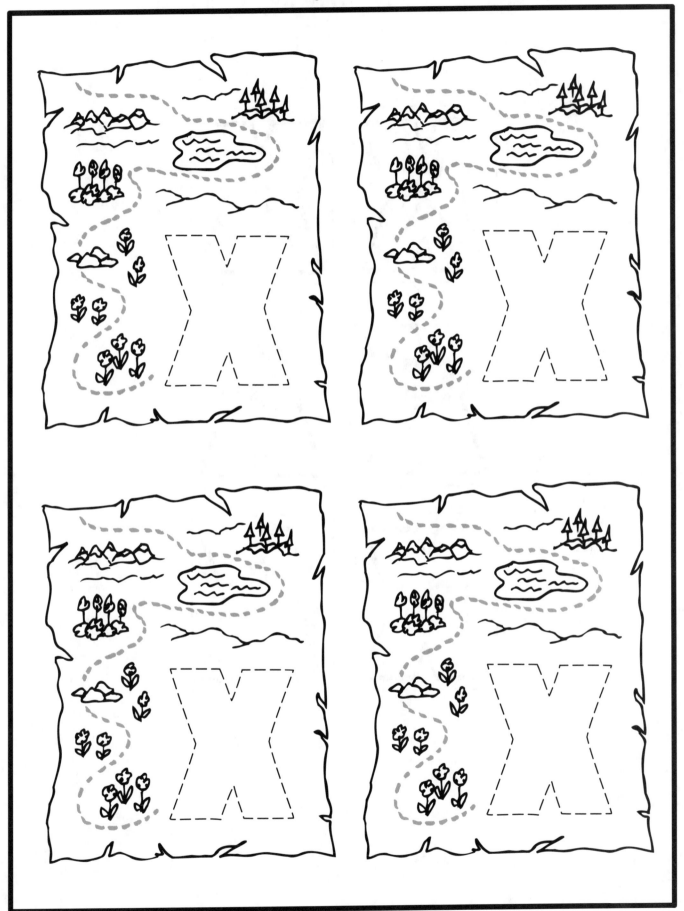

Letter X Cards

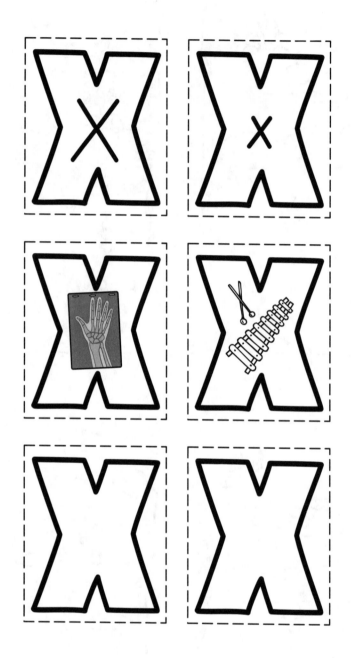

Basket of Yarn Match Board

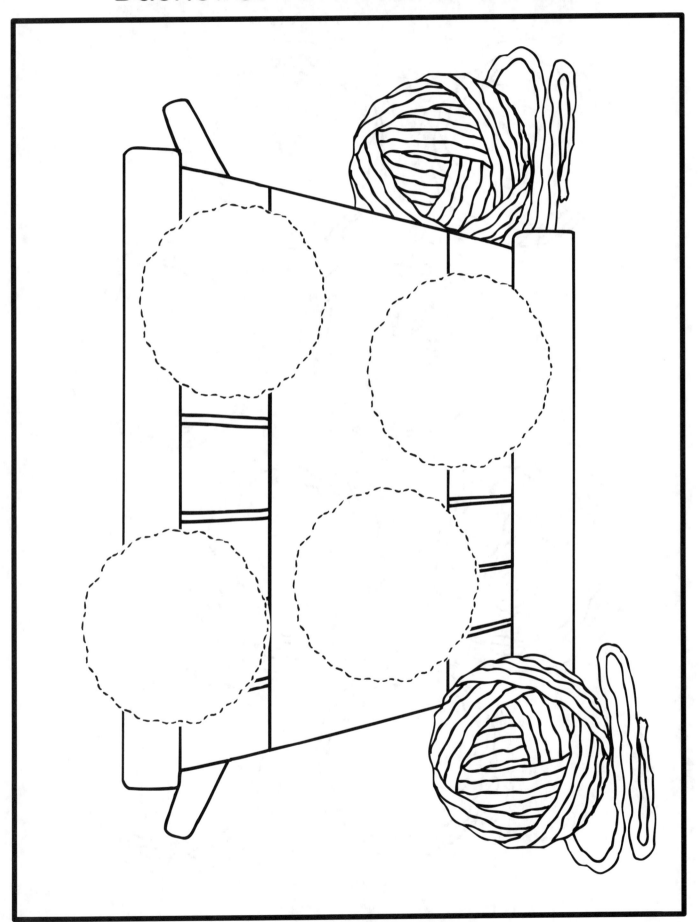

Yarn Ball Cards

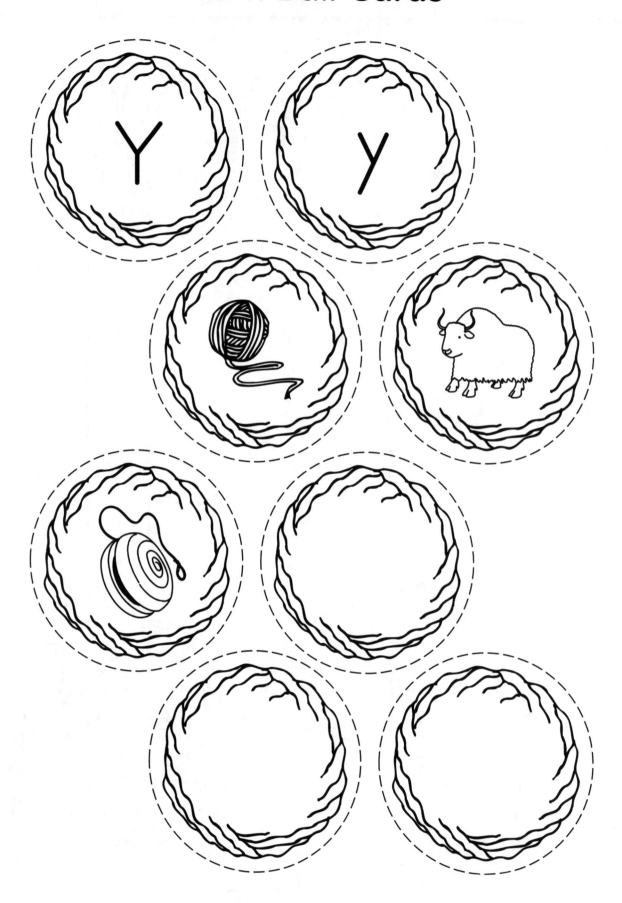

Zipper Pulls Match Board

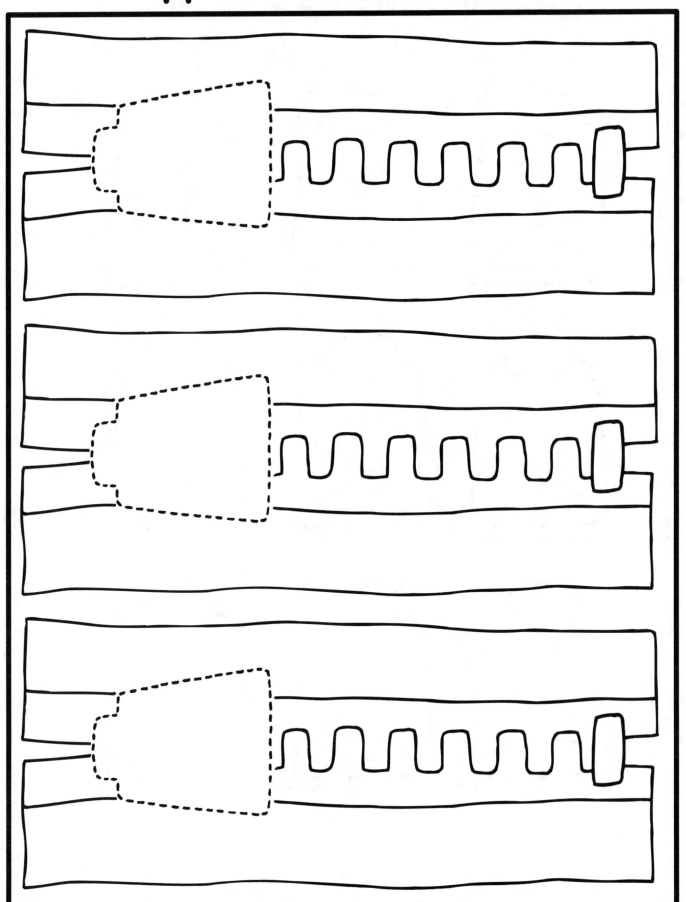

Zipper Pull Cards

Alphabet Match Board

	Aa	
Bb	Cc	Dd
Ee	Ff	Gg
Hh	Ii	Jj
Kk	Ll	Mm

Alphabet Match Board

	Nn	
Oo	Pp	Qq
Rr	Ss	Tt
Uu	Vv	Ww
Xx	Yy	Zz

Match Board Cards

Cereal Box Match-ups

Make cereal box Match-ups for children to practice alphabet skills.

Materials:

Match-ups boards and cards   scissors   crayons or markers
cereal boxes   glue   Velcro
colored construction paper

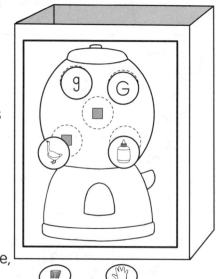

Cover a cereal box with colored construction paper. Reproduce, color, cut out, and glue a match board onto each side of the cereal box. Attach a Velcro square to the spaces on each match board. Program the blank cards of each matching card set, then reproduce, laminate, and cut out. Attach a Velcro square to the back of each card. Store the cards inside the cereal box. Place boxes in your alphabet skills practice center.

Children draw and attach cards to the correct match board.

Match-ups Vest

Provide children with brown grocery bags to make alphabet skills practice vests.

Materials:

Match-ups boards and cards   brown grocery bag   scissors   glue
crayons or markers   construction paper   Velcro

Recruit parent volunteers to help children make Match-ups vests from brown grocery bags. Each child will need a brown grocery bag and a set of Match-ups boards and cards.

Cut a slit along the center of one of the wide panels of a brown grocery bag. Cut two arm holes and a neckline. Provide children with match boards to color, cut out, and glue to the back of each of their vests. Attach Velcro squares to the spaces on the match board and each front vest panel. Program the blank cards of the matching card set, then reproduce, laminate, and cut out. Help children attach Velcro squares to the back of each card. Use a marker to write the matching upper- and lower-case letters on the left and right front of each child's Match-ups Vest. Have children attach cards to the front of their vests when they are not practicing alphabet matching.

Match-ups Wallpaper Quilt

Make a small, medium, or large Match-ups Wallpaper Quilt for children to practice alphabet matching skills.

Materials:

Match-ups boards and cards	scissors	crayons or markers
wallpaper squares	hole punch	yarn
colored construction paper	glue	Velcro

Reproduce and provide children with oak tag match boards to color and cut out. Measure and cut wallpaper squares large enough to fit one match board on each square with an ample margin. Glue each child's cut-out match board onto a wallpaper square. Attach Velcro squares to the spaces on each match board. Punch an even number of holes along all four sides of each quilt square. Use yarn to lace squares together to form an alphabet Match-ups Quilt.

Program the blank cards of each matching card set, then reproduce, laminate, and cut out. Attach a Velcro square to the back of each card. Store each set of cards in a construction paper pocket on the back of each matching quilt square. Display Match-ups Wallpaper Quilts in an alphabet skills practice center.

Match-ups Concentration

Make playing card sets for children to play alphabet Match-ups Concentration.

Materials:

Match-ups cards	index cards	scissors
crayons or markers	glue	resealable plastic bag
construction paper		

Reproduce two construction paper copies of each Match-ups card set. Cut out and glue each card to a small index card. Store matching sets in small resealable plastic bags for individual or small group play.

To play: Shuffle, then place all cards, face down, on a flat surface. Invite one child at a time to turn over two cards and identify each picture or letter. If there is a match, the player keeps the cards and play continues. If there is no match, the player turns the cards back over and another child takes a turn. Play continues until all the cards are taken.

Request for Craft Supplies

Dear Parent,

Please send supplies listed below to school with your child for our alphabet practice workstation.

- yarn
- ribbon
- twine
- shoelaces
- buttons
- pom poms

- resealable plastic bags
- cereal boxes (empty)
- brown grocery bags
- glitter
- glitter pens
- wiggle eyes
- sticky dots
- cotton balls
- sequins

- letter-size envelopes
- cotton swabs
- craft sticks
- index cards
- sand
- Velcro (adhesive)
- pipe cleaners
- wallpaper scraps

Thank you,

_____
Teacher

Match-ups • ©2004 Monday Morning Books, Inc.